Zoe the SoloBee

To Him,
Sing for The Bees!
Candac Vanderloff

10-12-18

Kapingamarangi Press ☉ San Diego 2016

Vanderhoff, C.L.
Zoe the SoloBee/C.L. Vanderhoff

Summary: Zoe, a female solitary native bee (Osmia aglaia) experiences her lifecycle.
Zoe collects pollen, builds a nest and lays eggs. One year
later the eggs hatch to repeat the cycle.

ISBN-978-0-9979100-0-1

Dedicated
to those who love and care for
our beloved Mother Earth and all
her creatures; the big, the small
and the tiny.

There was a little SoloBee,
　　　she flew so leisurely.

And when she found a flower blossom,
she rolled around with glee.

3

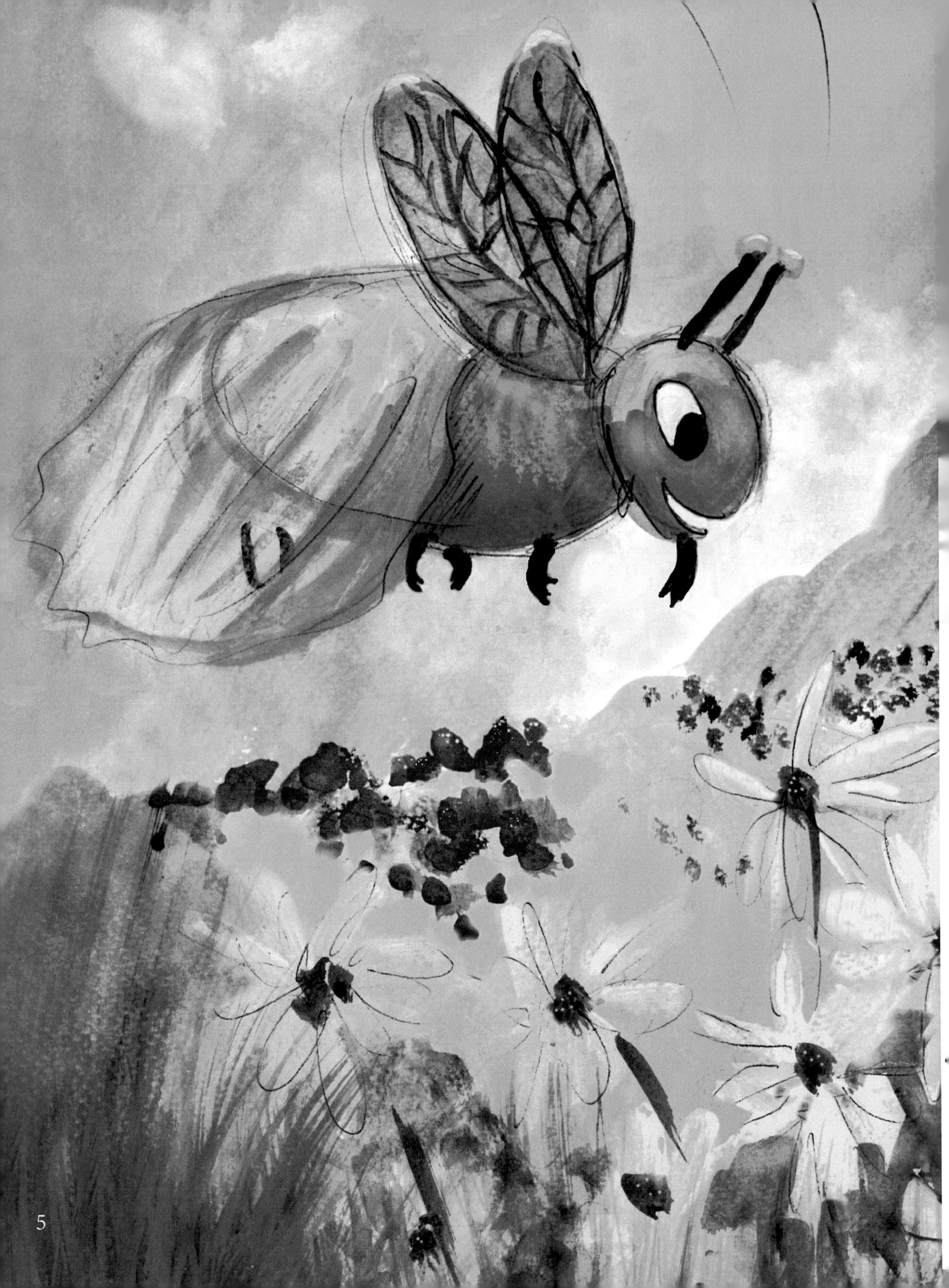

Dazzling in her cape of pollen,
she would fly back home.

And in her little cozy tunnel,
she marked it as her own.

In her little wooden tunnel,
     she rolled a ball of pollen.

9

Then she laid an egg, a girl!
a boy would always follow.

When she filled her tunnel nest,
she sealed up the door.

Then off to find
more flower blossoms,
and roll around some more.

In the fall, the winter cold,
waiting for the spring.

Hatching in the bright warm sun,
they all came out to sing.

If you love your juicy apple,
        if you love your pear.

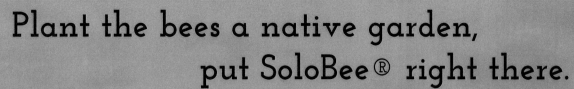

Plant the bees a native garden,
            put SoloBee® right there.

Zoe the SoloBee

Happy in her SoloBee® Shelter

25

Wherever you are,
you can...

Build a Bee Garden

1. Grow Flowering Plants
   A local nursery can suggest bee friendly
   natives, herbs, trees and shrubs.

2. Make a Bee Drinking-Pond
   Set stones in a dish of water.

3. Avoid Chemical Use
   Use organics for fertilizing
   and pest control.

4. Provide Shelter
   Place a bee shelter in
   a sunny spot.

More Resources
at SoloBee.com

26

The SoloBee Story

I grew up in rural Michigan where bees, flowers and water are abundant. That landscape compared to my new, drought-stricken Southern California garden seems like paradise to me now. Despite the lack of rain here, we managed to create a beautiful homestead with the help of some simple strategies, such as, greywater reuse and planting drought tolerant fruit trees and native plants. Like most gardeners, I was aware of the massive die-off of honeybees, but had no idea that the other 98% of bee species are suffering too. The other bee species, solitary native bees, are the subject of this book. Solitary bees live in tunnels in the ground and tunnels in trees, reeds or shells. If you have not heard of these non-stinging bees, you are not alone, I hadn't either, but I was curious to learn more. To find out if these bees did indeed live in our neighborhood I set out a bee shelter. Within two weeks the shelter was filled with bee eggs and the doors were capped with mud. What a surprise to know our native solo bees were in need of shelter. Watching the shelter fill up so quickly was the event that inspired the SoloBee Shelter Project. After months of research, we designed the shelters we sell today.

During product development, I met bee expert Keng-Lou James Hung. James has studied bees for over seven years and will soon complete a PhD. in Ecology. James encouraged me to create educational materials and the result is the SoloBee song. To teach my young niece Zoe the words, I created flashcards and those cards became this book. Soon Zoe will be singing her SoloBee Song! Today we are expanding our efforts by educating gardeners, farmers and school children about these prolific pollinators that are more effective at pollination than honeybees and are safe because they rarely sting. With 80% of all crops requiring pollination, these efficient little bees may be the solution to our pollination crisis.

Join us in becoming a SoloBee-keeper by adding flowers, water and shelter to your garden today!

C.L. Vanderhoff

Osmia aglaia
is a real green bee that pollinates fruit trees, vegetables and especially berries. This photograph was taken by Hartmut Wisch, a scientist who studies solitary native bees.

28

Solobee Song

Based on: The Itsy Bitsy Spider

Lyrics By:
Candy Vanderhoff

There was a lit-tle so-lo bee, she flew so lei-sure-ly, And when she found a flow-er bloss-om, She rolled a-round with glee. Daz-zl-ing in her cape of pol-len She would fly back home And in her lit-tle co-zy tun-nel, She marked it as her own. In her lit-tle wood-en tun-nel, she rolled a ball of pol-len. Then she laid an egg, a girl, A boy would al-ways foll-ow. Once she filled her tun-nel nest, She sea-led up the door. Then off to find more flow-er bloss-oms, and roll a-round some more. In the Fall the Win-ter cold wait-ing for the Spring. Hatch-ing in the bright warm sun, they all came out to sing. If you love your jui-cy app-le, If you love your pear. Plant the bees a nat-ive gar-den, Put Sol-o bee right there!

© 2015

Sound recording and SoloBee Sing-along song book at www. SoloBee.com

29